2 Describe fully each of the numbered and bracketed melodic intervals (e.g. majo

E. Ysaÿe, Sonata

Intervals:

1 ....

2 ....

3 ....

4 ....

5 ....

3 The following melody is written for horn in F. Transpose it *down* a perfect 5th, as it will sound at concert pitch. Do *not* use a key signature but remember to put in all necessary sharp, flat or natural signs.

Draeseke, Adagio for horn and piano, Op. 31

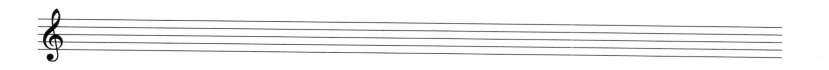

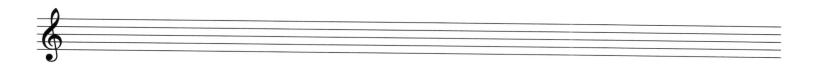

4 Look at this extract, which is from a song by Elgar, and then answer the questions that follow.

(a) (i) **Mark clearly on the music**, using the appropriate capital letter for identification, one example of each of the following. Also give the bar number of each of your answers, as shown in the answer to **A**.

10

From bar 5 onwards

   A in the soprano part, a sign that means accent the note.   Bar ....5....

   B in the piano part, a subdominant chord in root position
      (IVa) in the key of D major (circle the notes concerned).   Bar ....   (2)

   C a place where the soprano part sounds at a lower pitch than the
      top note of the right-hand piano part (circle the soprano note concerned).   Bar ....   (2)

   D in the right-hand piano part, a note that is *not*
      in the key of D major (circle the note concerned).   Bar ....   (2)

  (ii) Give the technical names (e.g. tonic, dominant) of the two notes in the soprano part marked **X** and **Y**. The key is D major.

    X (bar 4) ....   (2)

    Y (bar 7) ....   (2)

Music Theory Past Papers 2015

ABRSM Grade 5

Theory Paper Grade 5 2015 A

TOTAL MARKS
100

Duration 2 hours

This paper contains SEVEN questions, ALL of which should be answered.
Write your answers on this paper – no others will be accepted.
Answers must be written clearly and neatly – otherwise marks may be lost.

1 (a) Look at the following extract and then answer the questions below.

15

en dehors

Ibert, *Bajo la Mesa*

    (i)   The extract begins on the first beat of the bar. Put in the correct time signature.   (2)

    (ii)   Give the meaning of *en dehors*. ....   (2)

    (iii) Write as a breve (double whole-note) an enharmonic equivalent of the note marked ∗.

   (2)

(b) Look at the following extract and then answer the questions below.

Handel, *Alexander's Feast*, HWV 75

    (i)   Describe the chords marked ⌐A⌐, ⌐B⌐ and ⌐C⌐ as I, II, IV or V. Also indicate whether the lowest
note of the chord is the root (a), 3rd (b) or 5th (c). The key is A major.

    Chord **A** (bar 1)   ....   (2)

    Chord **B** (bar 1)   ....   (2)

    Chord **C** (bar 3)   ....   (2)

    (ii)   Rewrite the first left-hand note of the extract so that it sounds at the same pitch, but using
the alto C clef. Remember to put in the clef and the key signature.

   (3)

(b) (i) Give the meaning of:

10

ad lib. (soprano, bar 5) .... (2)

cantabile e con amore (soprano, bars 6–7) ....

.... (4)

(ii) Rewrite the two piano left-hand notes of bar 4 (marked └─────┘) so that they sound at the same pitch, but using the tenor C clef. Remember to put in the clef and the key signature.

(4)

(c) (i) Give the name of the voice part which lies between tenor and bass in vocal range.

10

.... (2)

(ii) Name a standard orchestral instrument that could play the soprano part of the extract so that it sounds at the same pitch, and state the family of instruments to which it belongs.

Instrument .... Family .... (4)

(iii) Now state whether the instrument you named above is a transposing or non-transposing instrument. .... (2)

(iv) Underline *one* instrument from the list below that is a member of the orchestral percussion family.

oboe   trombone   tambourine   cello   (2)

5

5 (a) Put sharps or flats in front of the notes that need them to form the scale of Bb **melodic** minor. Do *not* use a key signature.

(b) Write the key signature of four sharps and then one octave **descending** of the major scale with that key signature. Use semibreves (whole notes) and begin on the tonic.

6 EITHER

(a) Compose a complete melody for unaccompanied bassoon or cello, using the given opening. **Indicate the tempo and other performance directions**, including any that might be particularly required for the instrument chosen. The complete melody should be eight bars long.

Instrument for which the melody is written: ....

OR

(b) Compose a complete melody to the following words for a solo voice. Write each syllable under the note or notes to which it is to be sung. Also **indicate the tempo and other performance directions as appropriate**.

> The jolly god in triumph comes;
> Sound the trumpets, beat the drums!
>
> *John Dryden*

7 Suggest suitable progressions for two cadences in the following melody by indicating ONLY ONE chord (I, II, IV or V) at each of the places marked A–E. You do not have to indicate the position of the chords, or to state which note is in the bass.

Show the chords:

EITHER (a) by writing I, II etc. or any other recognized symbols on the dotted lines below;

OR (b) by writing notes on the staves.

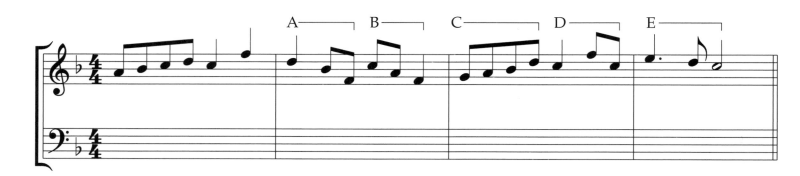

FIRST CADENCE:

Chord A ....

Chord B ....

SECOND CADENCE:

Chord C ....

Chord D ....

Chord E ....

Theory Paper   Grade 5   2015   B

Duration 2 hours

This paper contains SEVEN questions, ALL of which should be answered.
Write your answers on this paper – no others will be accepted.
Answers must be written clearly and neatly – otherwise marks may be lost.

TOTAL MARKS
100

1   Look at the following extract for violin, which begins on the first beat of the bar, and then answer the questions below.

15

J. Dont, Study, Op. 35 No. 5

etc.

(a) Describe the time signature as: simple or compound   ....   (1)

duple, triple or quadruple   ....   (1)

(b) Describe fully each of the numbered and bracketed melodic intervals (e.g. major 2nd).

1   ....   (2)

2   ....   (2)

3   ....   (2)

(c) The extract is in the key of G minor.
Which other key has the same key signature?   ....   (2)

(d) A violinist might be asked to play 'sul G' and this means   ....   (2)

(e) Rewrite the first note of the extract so that it sounds at the same pitch, but using the alto C clef.
Remember to put in the clef and the key signature.

(3)

2 This passage is for SATB choir, written in open score. Rewrite it in short score. 10

Lotti, Mass for four voices (adapted)

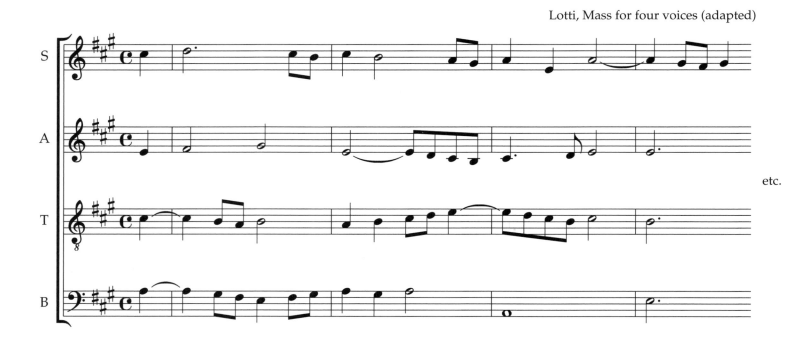

etc.

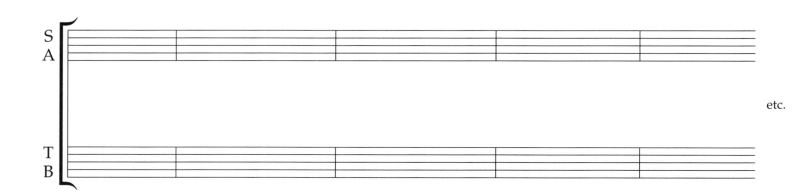

etc.

3 Look at this extract, which is from a piano piece by Kullak, and then answer the questions that follow. *Note that the left hand uses the treble clef throughout.*

(a) (i) Give the meaning of:

10

dolce .... (2)

tristamente .... (2)

sf (e.g. bar 4) .... (2)

(ii) Rewrite the last left-hand chord of the extract so that it sounds at the same pitch, but using the tenor C clef. Remember to put in the clef and the key signature.

(4)

(b) (i) Describe the chords marked ⌐X⌐ and ⌐Y⌐ as I, II, IV or V. Also indicate whether ☐10 the lowest note of the chord is the root (a), 3rd (b) or 5th (c). The key is F minor.

Chord **X** (bar 3) .... (2)

Chord **Y** (bar 4) .... (2)

(ii) Give the technical names (e.g. tonic, supertonic) of the two notes in the left-hand part marked **A** and **B**. Remember that the key is F minor.

A (bar 2) .... (2)

B (bar 4) .... (2)

(iii) Write as a breve (double whole-note) an enharmonic equivalent of the right-hand note of bar 2 (marked ↓).

(2)

(c) (i) The extract begins in the key of ☐10 F minor. In which key does it end? .... (2)

(ii) Name a standard orchestral woodwind instrument that could play the opening phrase of the right-hand part (marked ⌐_____⌐) so that it sounds at the same pitch.

Instrument .... (2)

(iii) Now name a *different* family of standard orchestral instruments and state its lowest-sounding member.

Family ....   Instrument .... (4)

(iv) Answer TRUE or FALSE to this statement:
A trumpeter might be asked to play pizzicato. .... (2)

4 (a) Using semibreves (whole notes), write one octave **descending** of the major scale that begins on the given note. Do *not* use a key signature but put in all necessary sharp or flat signs. [10]

(b) Using semibreves (whole notes), write one octave **ascending** of the **melodic** minor scale that has the given key signature. Begin on the tonic and remember to include any necessary additional sharp, flat or natural signs.

5 The following melody is written for clarinet in B♭. Transpose it *down* a major 2nd, as it will sound at concert pitch. Remember to put in the new key signature and add any necessary accidentals. [10]

Reger, Albumblatt, WoO II/13

(a) Compose a complete melody for unaccompanied oboe or trumpet, using the given opening. **Indicate the tempo and other performance directions**, including any that might be particularly required for the instrument chosen. The complete melody should be eight bars long.

Instrument for which the melody is written: ....

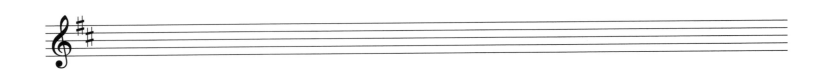

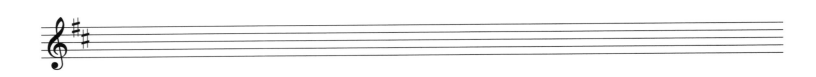

OR

(b) Compose a complete melody to the following words for a solo voice. Write each syllable under the note or notes to which it is to be sung. Also **indicate the tempo and other performance directions as appropriate**.

> The day is done, and the darkness
> Falls from the wings of Night.   *H. W. Longfellow*

7 Suggest suitable progressions for two cadences in the following melody by indicating ONLY ONE chord (I, II, IV or V) at each of the places marked A–E. You do not have to indicate the position of the chords, or to state which note is in the bass.

Show the chords:

EITHER   (a)   by writing I, II etc. or any other recognized symbols on the dotted lines below;

OR   (b)   by writing notes on the staves.

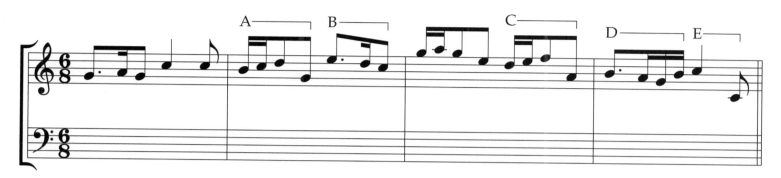

FIRST CADENCE:

Chord A   ....

Chord B   ....

SECOND CADENCE:

Chord C   ....

Chord D   ....

Chord E   ....

Theory Paper   Grade 5   2015   C

Duration 2 hours

This paper contains SEVEN questions, ALL of which should be answered.
Write your answers on this paper – no others will be accepted.
Answers must be written clearly and neatly – otherwise marks may be lost.

TOTAL MARKS
100

1 (a) Look at the following extract and then answer the questions below.

15

Haas, Suite for oboe and piano, Op. 17

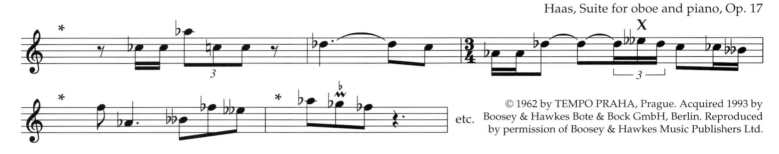

   (i)   The extract begins on the first beat of the bar and contains some changes of time signature.
         Put in the correct time signatures at the three places marked *.   (6)

   (ii) Write as a breve (double whole-note) an enharmonic equivalent of the note marked **X**.

(2)

(b) Look at the following extract and then answer the questions below.

X. Scharwenka, *Im Volkston*, Op. 62 No. 2

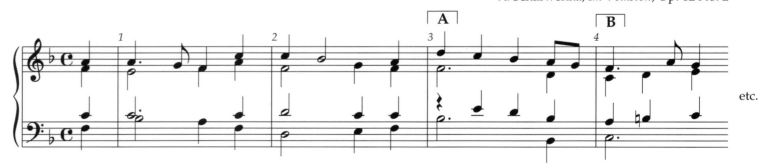

   (i)   Describe the chords marked ⌐A⌐ and ⌐B⌐ as I, II, IV or V. Also indicate whether the lowest
         note of the chord is the root (a), 3rd (b) or 5th (c). The key is F major.

         Chord **A** (bar 3)   ....   (2)

         Chord **B** (bar 4)   ....   (2)

   (ii) Rewrite the last right-hand chord of the extract so that it sounds at the same pitch, but
         using the alto C clef. Remember to put in the key signature.

(3)

16

2 Describe fully each of the numbered and bracketed melodic intervals (e.g. major 2nd). [10]

Delius, Double Concerto for violin, cello and orchestra, RT VII/5

Intervals:

1 ....

2 ....

3 ....

4 ....

5 ....

3 These are the actual sounds made by a clarinet in A. Rewrite the passage as it would appear for the player to read, that is, transpose it *up* a minor 3rd. Do *not* use a key signature but remember to put in all necessary sharp, flat or natural signs. [10]

Reger, *Variations and Fugue on a Theme by Mozart*, Op. 132

4 Look at this extract, which is from a piece for cello and piano by Fauré, and then answer the questions that follow.

(a) (i) Give the meaning of:

$\quad$ ♩. = 50 $\quad$ .... (2)

$\quad$ arco $\quad$ .... (2)

$\quad$ *sempre* (piano, bar 1) $\quad$ .... (2)

$\quad$ 10

(ii) Rewrite the last right-hand piano chord of the extract so that it sounds at the same pitch, but using the tenor C clef. Remember to put in the clef and the key signature.

$\quad$ (4)

(b) (i) Draw a bracket (⌐‾‾‾‾‾‾‾¬) over *four successive* notes in the cello part that form part of a chromatic scale.

$\quad$ 10

$\quad$ (2)

(ii) In bars 5–8 of the piano part, draw a circle around a subdominant chord in first inversion (IVb) in the key of G minor. (2)

(iii) Complete the following statement:

$\quad$ The cello notes of bar 8 can be found in the .... form of the scale of G minor. (2)

(iv) Give the technical names (e.g. tonic, dominant) of the two notes in the cello part marked **A** and **B**. The key is G minor.

$\quad$ **A** (bar 1) $\quad$ .... (2)

$\quad$ **B** (bar 3) $\quad$ .... (2)

(c) (i) Answer TRUE or FALSE to each of the following statements:

$\quad$ 10

$\quad$ The extract begins with an anacrusis (upbeat). $\quad$ .... (2)

$\quad$ The sign ⊓ tells a string player to use an up-bow. $\quad$ .... (2)

(ii) Underline *one* of the instruments listed below that could play the cello part of the extract so that it sounds at the same pitch.

$\quad\quad$ timpani $\quad\quad\quad$ bassoon $\quad\quad\quad$ oboe $\quad\quad\quad$ cymbals (2)

(iii) The cello is a member of the string family of orchestral instruments. Name a *different* family of standard orchestral instruments and state its highest-sounding member.

$\quad$ Family $\quad$ .... $\quad$ Instrument $\quad$ .... (4)

19

5 (a) Using semibreves (whole notes), write one octave **descending** of the **harmonic** minor [10] scale that has the given key signature. Begin on the tonic and remember to include any necessary additional sharp, flat or natural signs.

(b) Write one octave **ascending** of the scale of A♭ major. Do *not* use a key signature but put in all necessary sharp or flat signs. Use semibreves (whole notes) and begin on the tonic.

(a) Compose a complete melody for unaccompanied flute or violin, using the given opening. **Indicate the tempo and other performance directions**, including any that might be particularly required for the instrument chosen. The complete melody should be eight bars long.

Instrument for which the melody is written: ....

OR

(b) Compose a complete melody to the following words for a solo voice. Write each syllable under the note or notes to which it is to be sung. Also **indicate the tempo and other performance directions as appropriate**.

> Lo! I am come to autumn,
> When all the leaves are gold.   *G. K. Chesterton*

7 Suggest suitable progressions for two cadences in the following melody by indicating ONLY ONE chord (I, II, IV or V) at each of the places marked A–E. You do not have to indicate the position of the chords, or to state which note is in the bass.

Show the chords:

EITHER   (a)   by writing I, II etc. or any other recognized symbols on the dotted lines below;

OR   (b)   by writing notes on the staves.

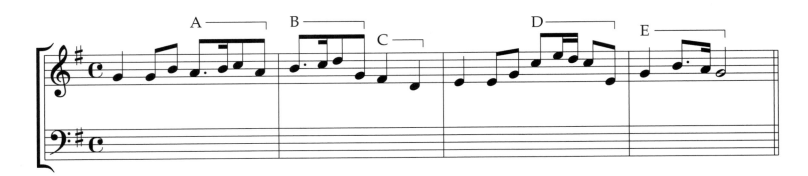

FIRST CADENCE: SECOND CADENCE:

Chord A   ....

                                                             Chord D   ....

Chord B   ....

                                                             Chord E   ....

Chord C   ....

Theory Paper   Grade 5   2015   S

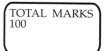

Duration 2 hours

This paper contains SEVEN questions, ALL of which should be answered.
Write your answers on this paper – no others will be accepted.
Answers must be written clearly and neatly – otherwise marks may be lost.

1 (a) Look at the following extract and then answer the questions below.

J. S. Bach, Goldberg Variations, No. 7, BWV 988

    (i)   Name the ornaments marked **A** and **B**.

          A (bar 3)   ....   (2)

          B (bar 8)   ....   (2)

    (ii)   Give the time name (e.g. crotchet or quarter note) of
          the *shortest* note in the extract (ignoring the ornaments).   ....   (2)

    (iii) Give the technical names (e.g. tonic, dominant) of the two notes marked **X** and **Y**.
          The key is G major.

          X (bar 4)   ....   (2)

          Y (bar 6)   ....   (2)

(b) Look at the following extract and then answer the questions below.

D. Scarlatti, Sonata in F, Kp. 297

    (i)   Rewrite the extract with the notes correctly grouped (beamed).   (3)

    (ii)   Describe the time signature as: simple or compound   ....   (1)

                                   duple, triple or quadruple   ....   (1)

TOTAL MARKS
100

15

2 Describe fully each of the numbered and bracketed melodic intervals (e.g. major 2nd). `10`

Spohr, Clarinet Concerto No. 3 in F minor

Intervals:

1 ....

2 ....

3 ....

4 ....

5 ....

3 The following melody is written for clarinet in B♭. Transpose it *down* a major 2nd, as `10`
it will sound at concert pitch. Do *not* use a key signature but remember to put in all
necessary sharp, flat or natural signs.

Hurlstone, No. 2 from *Four Characteristic Pieces* for clarinet and piano

4 Look at this extract, which is from a folksong arranged by Reger for SATB choir, and then answer the questions that follow.

(a) (i) Give the meaning of:

10

Mit Ausdruck   .... (4)

più (bar 6)   .... (2)

(ii) The extract is in the key of F major.
Which other key has the same key signature?   .... (2)

(iii) Draw a bracket (⌐￢) over *three successive* notes in the *tenor* part that
form part of a chromatic scale. (2)

(b) (i) Describe the chords marked ⌈X⌉, ⌈Y⌉ and ⌈Z⌉ as I, II, IV or V. Also indicate whether the lowest note of the chord is the root (a), 3rd (b) or 5th (c). Remember that the key is F major.

10

Chord **X** (bar 2) .... (2)

Chord **Y** (bar 5) .... (2)

Chord **Z** (bar 7) .... (2)

(ii) Rewrite the last tenor and bass notes of bar 2 (marked ↑) so that they sound at the same pitch, but using the tenor C clef. Remember to put in the clef and the key signature.

(4)

(c) (i) Write as a breve (double whole-note) an enharmonic equivalent of the first soprano note of bar 6 (marked ↓).

10

(2)

(ii) Give the name of the voice part which lies between soprano and alto in vocal range. .... (2)

(iii) Name a standard orchestral instrument that could play the soprano part of the extract so that it sounds at the same pitch, and state the family to which it belongs.

Instrument .... Family .... (4)

(iv) Now state whether the instrument you named above is a transposing or non-transposing instrument. .... (2)

5 (a) Write the key signature of four sharps and then one octave **descending** of the **melodic** minor scale with that key signature. Use semibreves (whole notes), begin on the tonic and remember to include any necessary additional sharp, flat or natural signs.

(b) Put sharps or flats in front of the notes that need them to form the scale of G♭ major. Do *not* use a key signature.

(a) Compose a complete melody for unaccompanied violin or trumpet, using the given opening. **Indicate the tempo and other performance directions**, including any that might be particularly required for the instrument chosen. The complete melody should be eight bars long.

Instrument for which the melody is written: ....

OR

(b) Compose a complete melody to the following words for a solo voice. Write each syllable under the note or notes to which it is to be sung. Also **indicate the tempo and other performance directions as appropriate**.

> I like the calm of the early fields,
> The ducks asleep by the lake.   *W. S. Blunt*

7 Suggest suitable progressions for two cadences in the following melody by indicating ONLY ONE chord (I, II, IV or V) at each of the places marked A–E. You do not have to indicate the position of the chords, or to state which note is in the bass.

Show the chords:

EITHER   (a)   by writing I, II etc. or any other recognized symbols on the dotted lines below;

OR   (b)   by writing notes on the staves.

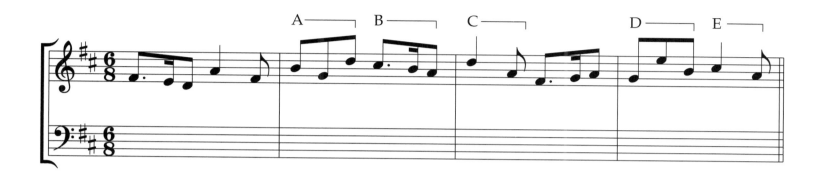

FIRST CADENCE:

Chord A   ....

Chord B   ....

Chord C   ....

SECOND CADENCE:

Chord D   ....

Chord E   ....

Music Theory Past Papers 2015

Four separate papers from ABRSM's 2015 Theory exams for Grade 5

- Essential practice material for all ABRSM Theory exam candidates
- Model answers also available

Support material for ABRSM Theory exams

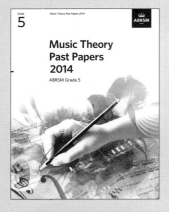

Published by ABRSM (Publishing) Ltd,
a wholly owned subsidiary of ABRSM

Cover by Kate Benjamin & Andy Potts
Printed in England by Halstan & Co. Ltd, Amersham, Bucks.,
on materials from sustainable sources

Reprinted in 2017

www.abrsm.org   f facebook.com/abrsm
 @abrsm   ▶ ABRSM YouTube

ISBN 978-1-84849-759-7

9 781848 497597